X

D1084220

F
Ba21   3 & 4 - Ad.

77

THE LOST URANIUM MINE

By
Henry Bamman
Robert Whitehead

Illustrations
Berthold Tiedemann

BENEFIC PRESS • CHICAGO

Publishing Division of Beckley-Cardy Company

Atlanta   Dallas   Long Beach   Portland

WHY? WHAT? WHERE?

Mark and Rich help an old miner named Patrick find a lost uranium mine deep in the Rocky Mountains near the town of Great Bear.

The Lost Uranium Mine

Hunting Grizzly Bears

Fire on the Mountain

City Beneath the Sea

The Search for Piranha

Sacred Well of Sacrifice

Library of Congress
Number 63-15509

Printed in the United States of America

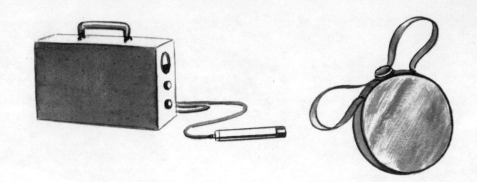

Contents

The Trail to Great Bear

At first, the snow fell softly on the three men. But soon it stormed down on them, carried along by a roaring wind. Mark could not see very far in the heavy snow. It was getting hard to see just where the trail climbed up into the mountains. Soon the trail would be lost in the snow.

"It's a bad storm!" called Mark, turning to the young man behind him.

"It should blow over soon," Rich called back, closing his eyes as he faced into the storm. "Let's keep going. If we stop now, we can't make it to Great Bear by dark. This storm is slowing us down too much."

Mark took a long look at the sky over the mountains. Then he turned and looked back down the trail. He could just see old Patrick fighting his way along through the snow. The old man was having a hard time climbing up the trail.

"Patrick can't go on much longer in this, Rich," said Mark. He pointed to the older man. Then he turned and called out into the wind, "Patrick!"

The older man stopped and looked up, brushing the snow from his eyes. Mark pointed to the sky over his head. Patrick nodded and began to walk faster up the trail.

Mark and Rich, along with their good friend Patrick, were on their way to the ghost town of Great Bear, deep in the Rocky Mountains. Patrick, an old miner, had asked Mark and Rich to help him find a lost uranium mine near the little mountain town.

It was not long before Patrick reached the side of his two young friends.

"We have to . . . get in . . . out of this . . . storm, Patrick," Mark said. "We just can't go on. . .in this snow." He turned and pointed to a dark spot a little way up the side of the mountain and back from the snowy trail.

"Look!" Mark said. "See that opening . . . in the face of the mountain up there. It looks like it's a . . . cave. Let's see if we can climb . . . up there."

"Just as . . . well that we do," Patrick said. "Right now . . . we can't get . . . very far . . . in this storm."

As if to make sure that the men did not go on, the wind roared down on them again. The snow came blowing into their faces and eyes. It was so bad now, that they could see only a little of the trail that climbed up the mountain before them.

"Come on!" called Mark, "before we can't even . . . find our way . . . up to that cave." And he headed off the trail up toward the rocks above.

The opening that Mark had spotted was above and to the right of the trail. He thought it would make a good place in which to wait out the storm.

"We can't make it to Great Bear in this storm," Mark thought. "Patrick can't fight this snow and wind much longer. And these Geiger-counters are getting too heavy for Rich and me to carry."

The men had found it very hard to climb up the mountain trail facing into the wind. But now, off the trail, the snow was deeper. Climbing was even slower and harder. Looking back, Mark found Rich right behind him. But far down the trail came Patrick, who had dropped back again.

As Mark slowed to wait for Patrick, Rich came up and stood by his side. The two men were very good friends. Mark was a young man with big, soft eyes and a friendly laugh.

Rich was younger than Mark, but he stood a little taller. His face was deeply marked from fighting the mountain winds. He was a big man and he liked to eat.

"Some storm!" Rich said.

"Don't just talk about it," called Mark. "Do something!"

Mark stood away from the rocky side of the mountain. He looked up into the blowing snow, trying to see the opening above them.

He was suddenly surprised to see something dark drop down behind a rock at the mouth of the cave. He brushed the snow from his eyes and looked again.

There! There it was!

Turning excitedly to Rich, Mark called out, "Rich, did you see that?"

"See what?" asked Rich.

Mark pointed up the mountain to the cave. "Up there. Behind those rocks. See that. . ." Then he stopped. There was nothing there now. Who or what he saw was gone.

Just then, Patrick came up behind them. "Now how far to the cave?" asked the old miner.

"It is not too far now," said Rich.

Suddenly they heard a crash over their heads. The three men looked up toward the cave.

"What was that?" asked Rich.

"I don't know, but it was . . . right above us," Patrick said.

Hardly had the old man said it when there came another crash. A great roar rocked the place where the men stood.

Then, before their very eyes, rocks and snow began to drop down the side of the mountain.

Rocks and snow fell toward them. It looked as if all the mountain above them had suddenly given way. On they came, closer and closer. Faster and faster they fell down the side of the mountain.

Mark just had time to call, "Out of the way!" Then the snow and rocks crashed into them. The men fell head first back down the side of the mountain. Over and over they went, carried along by the crashing rocks and snow.

(918)

The Ghost

As suddenly as it began, the heavy storm of rocks and snow ended. Nothing but the roar of the wind and a dust-like snow fell about the men.

"Patrick! Rich! Are you all right?" Mark called, as he climbed out from under the heavy snow.

"Help me up!" called the old man.

By now Rich had worked his way out from under the snow, too. The two men ran to Patrick's side and pulled him out from under the deep snow.

"I'm all right," said Patrick, as he stood and brushed the snow from his eyes and face. "But how about you two. Are you all right?"

"We are all right, too," said Rich. "I don't know how, but those rocks brushed right by us."

"How are the Geiger-counters?" asked Patrick.

"All right," said Rich. "Here are. . ."

"Listen!" said Mark. "Do you hear something?"

The men listened. Then, from far above them, came a cold, ghostly laugh. It was just a little laugh, carried along by the wind. But it was a laugh, of that they were sure. Then the laugh was gone, lost in the noise of the roaring storm.

"Mark, there's a man up there who just tried to kill us," said Rich excitedly. "Come on! Let's go after him!" With that, Rich turned and headed back up the side of the mountain toward the cave.

"Wait, Rich!" Mark called after him.

But Rich was climbing up toward the cave, and nothing could stop him. A man had tried to kill them, and Rich was not going to let him get away.

When Mark saw that Rich was not going to stop, he went after him. Patrick tried to keep up, but he was soon left far behind.

Mark soon reached Rich. Then side by side the two men made their way up the mountain, winding in and out through the rocks.

"What do you . . . make of that laugh we heard?"
Rich asked.

"I don't know," Mark called out, "but. . . ." He
stopped suddenly, for there, right before them, was
the cave! Its dark mouth stood out even through the
blowing snow.

The two men stood still, listening. They could hear
nothing, nothing but the wind. Then eyeing the
opening in the mountain before them, the men walked
toward it. Making their way slowly, they looked behind
the rocks that were near the cave's opening. There
was nothing there.

Mark and Rich made their way to the black mouth of the cave. It was very dark and still. Rich turned on his light as they went in. He pointed the light up and down the sides of the cave. Here and there drops of water ran down over the dark rock.

While Rich looked about the mouth of the cave, Mark went on back into the dark cave.

"What did you find?" Rich called to him.

"There's some old wood back here," Mark called. "But that's all."

Mark and Rich were just coming out of the cave when Patrick came around the rocks near the opening. "Did you find something?" he called.

"No!" said Rich. "There's not a thing in there."

"But I'm sure there was," said Mark. "When we first came up the trail to the cave, I'm sure I saw something up here."

"What did you see?" asked Patrick.

"Well, I don't know," said Mark. "It was like a . . . a . . . well, if you must know, a ghost!"

"A ghost, my eye!" said Rich. "That was no ghost I heard. That was a man laughing!"

"Well, I still think. . ." Mark began, but Patrick stopped him.

"I know what it was," Patrick said softly. "There is only one thing it could have been. It was the 'Ghost of Great Bear'!"

(623)

Talk of a Mine

"That's better," said Rich when they were done eating and were sitting by the fire.

"Not bad. Not bad at all," said Mark. "But tell me one thing. How did you get this far without having something to eat, Rich?"

"Well, it was hard to do," laughed Rich.

The three men had walked into the cave to wait out the storm. Soon Rich had a good fire going. He made it from some of the old wood that Mark had found at the back of the cave.

"Now, Patrick. What's this about the 'Ghost of Great Bear'?" asked Mark.

"Well," began the old man, "the ghost is something that has been seen in and about Great Bear for a long, long time. All of the miners talked about it. Many of them said they had seen it in the mines. Others said it walked through the streets of the town at night."

"What is it the ghost of?" asked Mark.

"It's the ghost of a miner killed in a mine cave-in," said Patrick. "The man went looking for gold. He found some, and then he was killed for the gold. His killing was made to look like a cave-in. Now it's said that the ghost of the old miner walks about the town looking for his killer."

"Have you seen the ghost of the miner, Patrick?" Rich laughed softly.

"Sure have!" said the old miner. "And so has Mark. Right, Mark?"

"I saw something up here all right," said Mark. "But a ghost? I don't know."

"But what about that rock and snow that fell on us?" said Rich. "And that laugh? That was no ghost's laugh. That was a man's laugh."

"But where is the man now?" asked Patrick.

Mark and Rich did not know where the man was. And as they listened to Patrick talk, they began to think that they must have heard a ghost.

22

Soon the talk around the fire turned to uranium. "Tell us about that uranium mine we are looking for, Patrick," said Mark.

"Well, you know that our country has been looking for uranium for a long time," Patrick began. "They mine the ore. The money you get for finding the ore is very good. So, a while back, I thought I would go out and try to find some.

"I got a Geiger-counter like the ones we have with us. Then off I went, way back here into the mountains near Great Bear. I had hunted gold up around here a long time back. But then I heard there was uranium to be found up here. That's how I got to know Jim and heard about his uranium mine."

"Is Jim the man that you were telling us about, Patrick?" asked Mark.

"That's right," said Patrick. "Jim found uranium the day I got to Great Bear. That night, two men tried to kill him for his find. I helped Jim in the fight and he took me in as a friend.

"But Jim did not let me know where the uranium was down in the mine. He said no one would want to kill me if I did not know where the uranium was.

"Jim's find was a good one. He said it would take two to three days to mark it off. So while Jim worked in the mine, I stood watch near the opening."

Patrick went on, "On the last day, the men that Jim had the fight with found out what mine we were working. They came hunting for us. I spotted them coming and ran back into the mine to tell Jim."

"Did you find him?" Rich asked the old man.

"In a way I did," said Patrick. "It was a big mine with tunnels running all over. Jim could hear me calling for him. He came running from way back in the mine. He said the thing to do was for one of us to hide with the Geiger-counter while the other tried to lead the men away.

"Jim went back down
into the mine to hide the
Geiger - counter. I went
running out of the mine
through a little side tunnel. The men heard me and
came running after me. That was as near as I got
to the uranium ore find."

"What about Jim?" asked Rich.

"Jim was killed by a cave-in that day," said the old
miner. "After I got away from the men, I came back
looking for him. I found him in one of the side tunnels
near the mouth of the mine. Some wood and rocks had
dropped on him. He had a bad blow on the head. He
tried to tell me something about 'black ore'. Then he
was gone."

"Black ore?" said Rich. "What's that?"

"That's what uranium ore looks like," said Mark. "It's very black."

"Right!" said Patrick. "I looked all over down there for black ore. But there were so many tunnels I could not look in all of them. That's why I asked you two to go back there with me. I know there's some very good uranium ore down there, and it's all ours. All we have to do is find it."

"That's what we came for!" said Mark.

The men talked on for a while about the uranium and the ghost. But it was not too long before their heads began to nod. Soon they were sleeping. (906)

The Ghost Town

When the men left the cave with the first light of day, they found that the heavy snowstorm was over. The cold wind had dropped off, and only a soft snow fell about their heads. Working their way down through the rocks, the men found their way back to the trail and were soon making their way along it.

From time to time, Mark stopped to look to the right and left of the trail. "What are you looking for?" asked Rich. "Our ghost friend?"

"I'm not too sure, Rich," said Mark slowly. "But I have a feeling that we are being watched."

"Oh, come off it, Mark," said Rich. "There are no ghosts. You know that."

"I know," said Mark, "but still. . ."

"Come on," said Rich, walking around Mark and on up the trail. "The sooner we get to Great Bear, the sooner we get to that uranium."

For a long time, the men walked along the trail that was heavy with snow. The day was well along when the men made their way over the mountain top. The trail down the other side of the mountain was not as snowy, and they made much better time.

Just as night came, Patrick found an old trail leading off into the town of Great Bear. "What's the place like, Patrick?" asked Rich, as the three men headed down through the brush toward the town.

"It's just a little place. Some old buildings, that's all," said Patrick. "No one is here now, I'm sure. In the old days it was a very exciting place. But then the gold mines gave out. That killed the town. Now it's. . . well, it's ghostly."

The night was very dark and cold now. After going a little way, Patrick stopped. "What's up, Patrick?" asked Mark.

"There it is!" said the old man, pointing with his light. "Great Bear!"

And so it was. There in the point of Patrick's light stood some old buildings, dark and ghost-like in the cold night.

"Listen!" said Patrick.

The men stood side by side in the dark night and listened. The night was very still. The wind worked its way through the brush, blowing a light snow into their faces. The call of an animal came from far away. But that was all.

"What is it, Patrick?" asked Rich softly. "I don't hear a thing."

"Listen!" said Patrick again.

They listened again. But all they heard was the wind blowing through the brush.

At last, Mark said, "Well, if it was something, it's gone now." Then he turned to Patrick. "What about this mine, Patrick? You said it was just a little way out of town. But where?"

"I'm not too sure," Patrick said. "It's been some time and in the dark, one end of the town looks like the other."

Mark looked at his watch. Then he said, "The night's well along. Let's go on into Great Bear and look things over. We will have to find a place to sleep for the night."

"Good!" said Patrick. "I'm all for that. How about you, Rich?"

"All right with me," Rich said. "This Geiger-counter is getting heavy."

The town before them was very still. Mark and
Rich turned on their lights, and the men watched as
they trailed down the street of the old ghost town.
"Patrick was right," thought Mark. "The gold is gone.
So are the men. Time stands still here now."

As the men walked down the street, their lights fell
on some of the old buildings of the little town. The
first building the men came to was made of rocks
placed one on the other. By its side stood a building
made from cans placed end on end. One or two were
fire-blackened buildings, just dark spots under the
snow. Here and there along the street were other
buildings like these.

"Let's see if we can find a better one than that!"
said Mark. He pointed to a building that stood out
in his light. Two of its sides had caved in.

The men headed on down the street. There were
no walks, and they had to keep an eye out for brush
and old cans under the snow. Here and there the
men looked down little side streets. But the streets
were ghostly places of one or two buildings, and the
men did not go very far.

"I keep feeling eyes watching me," said Mark, as
he suddenly pointed his light behind him. But there
was nothing there, nothing but a trail through the
snow where they had walked.

Near the end of the
street, the men came to the
town well. The men saw
there was water in it.
"Let's look in one of the buildings along here," said
Patrick. "We would be close to water if we found a
place near here to sleep."

"Here's one!" called Rich. He ran his light over
a dark building close by. He went in the building and
soon came back out.

"Come on in," he called to Mark and Patrick. "This
building has a floor in it."

Mark and Patrick walked up to the door of the old
building and went in.

The door of the old building was still in place, rocking and nodding in the night wind. The building was a ghostly place, dark and still, with dust all about. But it did have a floor.

"What do you think, Patrick?" asked Mark.

"Looks all right to me," said Patrick.

Mark said, "I think we had better turn in for the night, then. This has been a long day."

"Right," said Patrick. "We should be up with the first light of day. I'm still not sure where the mine is. If we find the mine right away, then we can look for that black ore. And when we find that, we can mark off the mine as ours. Then we can be on our way by night."

"That's for me!" said Rich. "Uranium and money, just what I want."

"Uranium, money—and food!" laughed Mark.

Then the three men made a place to sleep on the floor of the old building. Soon all was still. (1022)

The Ghost Again

A long time after the men had turned in for the night, Mark was still not sleeping. He was sleepy, but he could not sleep. For one thing, the floor was very hard. For another, he could not stop thinking about nearly being killed out on the mountain trail the day before. "Where did that ghostly laugh come from? Was it the wind? It could have been."

But there were other things, too. Why did he have this feeling that they were being watched? And if they were being watched, was Patrick's "Ghost of Great Bear" doing it?

"But there are no ghosts," he thought. "We all know that. Then it must be a man. But why is he after us? For the uranium? And if he did try to kill us, how did he know we were coming up the trail? And how did he get away from the cave?

"Well, I can't work it all out now," he thought. "I should get some sleep."

Mark was just about to drop off to sleep when he heard a strange noise out in the night. He listened. The noise was not too far away.

Mark looked over at Patrick. The old man was sleeping. Then he turned to Rich, who had his eyes closed, too. He called softly, "Rich."

"Wha . . . What is it?" said Rich, turning over.

"Listen!" said Mark. "Hear that?"

The strange noise came again, much nearer now. But they could not tell for sure what it was. "What do you think it is?" asked Rich.

"I don't know," said Mark.

"Then go back to sleep," said Rich, turning over again. "It's nothing."

"A ghost is 'nothing' too," Mark said.

"A ghost!" said Rich, sitting up.

"Let's go have a look," Mark said.

The street before the men was dark and still. They could just see the buildings at the far end of the street. The buildings were great, dark things in the black night. Now and then the wind brushed up the snow. But that was all.

"Let's go on down the street," said Mark. "I'm sure I heard something out here!"

Slowly, Mark and Rich made their way down the street. They went from building to building, stopping now and then to look in the places where something could hide. But they saw nothing.

They were coming to the end of the street, when suddenly, Mark stopped. His mouth dropped open in surprise. "Rich! Look!" he called out.

At the far end of the street was a little snow hill. The hill was near the trail they had taken into the town that night. At the side of the hill, in the point of Mark's light, stood a ghost!

The 'thing' had the head of a man, but Mark and Rich could see right through much of it. The ghost's eyes were deep in its head, and they looked right at the men. The ghostly head nodded slowly up and down, up and down.

"The 'Ghost of Great Bear'!" Rich said to Mark.

"Keep still and watch!" said Mark. "Let's see what it is going to do."

The two men just stood there. They could not keep their eyes off the ghostly face.

Mark tried to fight off the thought that here was a ghost, right before his eyes. "There are no ghosts, there are no ghosts," he said over and over softly. "But here is one right before me."

The 'thing' gave a long, ghostly laugh. It rocked from side to side. Then slowly, it began to back away. The lighted face began to trail away in the dark night. The ghost became harder and harder to see. Then it was gone!

"Let's go get him!" said Rich.

"I'm with you!" Mark called out.

The two young men ran up the street, headed right for the spot where the ghost had stood. When they reached the hill, they stopped. For there, in the point of their lights, was nothing! There was no ghost, no man, and no place where one could hide!

(679)

The Cave-In

The three hunters were up with the first light of day. Patrick said he thought the mine was at the far end of the town. "I think there are two or three trails leading off into the mountains at that end of town," he said.

"Well, let's try one of them," Mark said.

With Patrick in the lead, the men headed into the mountains again. As they walked, Mark and Rich gave Patrick their news about the 'ghost' hunt they had gone on in the night.

It was not long before the men found a trail leading up through the rocks, just as Patrick had said. While winding in and out through the rocks, the men spotted a mine in the side of a hill. It was just an opening in the hard rock. An old ladder ran down into the dark mine.

Rich pointed his light down into the opening. "Let's try it!" he said to Mark and Patrick.

Rich climbed down the ladder first. Then came Mark, and last, Patrick. Mark and Rich helped the older man climb down.

Turning their lights from side to side, the men could see that they were in a very old mine. No work had been done here for a long time, for the rocky floors were heavy with dust.

"Do you think this is it, Patrick?" asked Mark, as he let his light trail along the sides of the mine.

"No, it's too little," said the old miner. "It's sure cold in here, though. Let's go back up."

"Wait!" called Rich. "Here's something!"

While Mark and Patrick had been talking near the ladder, Rich had walked to the far side of the mine. Now his light pointed to an opening where a little tunnel ran back into the rock. Mark and Patrick walked over to look at it.

"It leads back into the rock just a little way," Rich said. "I'm going to take a look."

Before Mark or Patrick could stop him, Rich had climbed into the opening. Mark called after him, "Come on back, Rich. There's nothing in there."

"Now just wait," Rich called back. He was still for some time. Then he called out, "There's another opening back here, but a big rock is in the way, and I can't get through. I can see on down the tunnel behind it, though."

"Come on, Rich. Give it up," Mark called again.

"No, Mark, I can get through," Rich said. "Just find something for me to work with so I can get this rock out of the way."

Patrick laughed softly and said to Mark, "There's no stopping him now. Come on. I saw some old wood over there by the ladder. Let's get it."

As the two men came near the ladder, Mark heard a noise above them. He looked up just in time to see the light coming through the mine opening above them suddenly go out. A great roar rocked the mine.

Mark pulled Patrick back against the side of the
mine just as the rocks above the ladder gave way.
With a roar, rocks and wood came crashing down from
above. The ladder fell to the floor of the mine. As it
fell, it brushed against the two men. The noise roared
through the cave.

Then as suddenly as it began, the cave-in was over.
The men turned their lights this way and that about
the mine. It was hard for them to see with all the
dust blowing around them. Pointing their lights to a
spot above them, the men could see that the opening
was now closed off. Leading down from it was a hill
of rocks that stood well over their heads.

Back in the tunnel, Rich heard the roar when the mine opening caved in. He backed his way out slowly. When he climbed out of the tunnel, he could hardly see with all the dust in the air.

"Mark! Patrick! Where are you?" he called.

"Over here!" Mark called out. "Keep back against the side of the mine, Rich. Patrick and I will come around to you."

Slowly, Mark and Patrick worked their way along the side of the mine. Soon they saw Rich's light through the dusty air.

"What did you two do?" asked Rich.

"Nothing," said Patrick. "All of a sudden the mine just caved in."

"How bad is it?" asked Rich.

"Very bad," said Mark. "All of the mine opening fell in. It's closed off all the way."

"Well, there is one thing we can do," said Rich. "I got that rock out of the way in the side tunnel. We can try that way."

"You lead the way, Rich," said Mark. "And let's turn out all but one of our lights. They will last longer that way."

With Rich in the lead, the men climbed into the opening in the side of the mine. One by one, they began to work their way along the tunnel.

The men found that the tunnel was very cold and dusty. When one man brushed against the side of the tunnel, the others were soon eating dust.

They soon reached the spot where Rich had pulled the big rock to one side, making a place for a man to get through. One at a time, they worked their way around it. Then on they went through the tunnel.

For a long time, the men made their way along the rocky floor of the tunnel. The climb was hard, and they had to stop now and then. All the while, the tunnel went up, little by little.

Coming to a turn in the tunnel, Rich suddenly stopped. "Do you feel something?" he called back to Mark and Patrick.

"No, I don't," said Patrick.

"Where?" asked Mark.

"Up here," said Rich. "Near my face."

Mark climbed along the tunnel to Rich's side. "Cold air!" he said.

"Right!" said Rich. "There must be an opening right around here."

Rich turned his light on the tunnel above him. He could see a dark place in the rock. "Look at that," he said, pointing to the place. "Just feel that cold air. It looks like a rock fell into an opening here."

"Here, Rich, let me have your light," said Mark. "See if you can get that rock out the opening."

Rich took the Geiger-counter from his back. With his light, Mark pointed out the rock for Rich. Rich placed his back against the rock. It was a big one, but Rich found he could turn it a little. Suddenly, dust fell into Rich's face.

"Look out, Rich!" Mark called.

Rich just had time to turn and climb up the tunnel before the rock came crashing to the tunnel floor. A great storm of dust and snow came blowing into the tunnel, carried along by the wind. Mark turned his eyes away.

When Mark looked back again, he could see some light coming through the opening to the tunnel where the rock had been.

Mark's first thought was of Rich. "Rich, are you all right?" he called.

"I'm great!" Rich said. "We have found a way out of here. Come on!"

With that, Rich climbed up through the opening and pulled Patrick up after him. Then came Mark with Rich's Geiger-counter. The men stood in the cold air. The sky above them was heavy with snow.

"Um-m, that feels good!" said Patrick.

"It looks good, too, after that dark tunnel," said Mark. "But I don't like the looks of that sky. We could be in for a bad storm." (1265)

50

Black Ore!

"Well, what now?" asked Rich, as he brushed the snow from his eyes.

"From the looks of that sky, we had better get back to town," said Mark.

"Which way do we go, Patrick?" asked Rich.

"Well, I'm not sure," said the old man. "But I think Great Bear is over this way." He pointed to a trail that headed off to the left through the rocks.

"We have to try something," said Mark. "Come on, men. Let's go!"

With Mark in the lead, the three men went off down the trail, one close behind the other. The wind was blowing against them from all sides. The mountains were soon lost in the blowing snow that was all around them. And it was cold, very cold.

"This is a bad storm!" Patrick called.

"What if we can't find our way out of here before night?" asked Rich.

"We have to, that's all," Mark called back.

It was very hard to keep on the trail now. At times the men lost it, but found it again behind some rocks where the wind had not carried the snow.

They walked on and on, facing right into the storm. The snow closed in on them from all sides. It fell so fast that the men had a hard time seeing one another on the trail.

Suddenly, Mark stopped. Rich and Patrick came up behind him. "What's up?" Rich asked.

"I think I have lost the trail!" Mark called out, pointing down to the snow.

The men stood in the deep snow and looked about them. Mark was right. There was no trail there. Looking up, they could make out the rocky face of a mountain. Looking down, they could see a dropoff that fell into nothing as far as the eye could see. The trail was gone.

"Well . . . which way . . .?" Rich began. Then he stopped talking, for the wind seemed to slow down suddenly. Through the blowing snow, Rich saw a dark opening in the side of the mountain above them. "A cave!" he called out excitedly, pointing up the side of the mountain.

"Come on, men," Mark said, "And make it fast. It's getting colder and colder out here."

One by one, the three men climbed up over the rocks as fast as they could. The cave was not far, and they soon reached it. There they dropped slowly to the rocky floor.

Mark pointed his light toward the back of the cave. There he could see another tunnel leading back into the rocks. "What is this place, Patrick?" asked Mark, running his light up the side of the cave.

"It looks like just an old cave to me," said Patrick, "but I can't tell for sure."

"Well, we can't wait here near the opening. It's too cold," said Mark. "Let's have a look around back there. It could be a mine, and there could be uranium."

Very slowly, the men began making their way back into the dark cave. It was very still in the tunnel now that they were walking away from the mine opening and the wind. But it was not as cold. Here and there they found side tunnels that ran off into the dark rock. The men went a little way into one or two of the tunnels, but they saw nothing that looked like uranium ore.

They had been making their way along the tunnel for some time when it slowly became bigger and much deeper. Suddenly, it opened out into another cave.

The men stopped, letting their lights trail along the floor of the cave. Just then, a roar came through the tunnel. They stood very, very still. They could feel something close to them, something that they could not see.

"What was that?" Rich asked.

The men heard the noise again over to the left. Turning their lights that way, the men were surprised to see a big, sleepy bear turning slowly toward them. To the men, the bear's eyes seemed to be full of fire. "Man!" said Rich.

"He's a big one!" Patrick said.

The bear let out another roar and stood up, fighting to brush the sleep from his eyes. "Keep your light on him," said Mark. "That should slow him down."

Mark ran his light along the side of the cave. His light stopped on a dark opening in the rock. "Another tunnel!" he called.

"Let's try it," said Rich. "Get going, you two! I don't think I can keep him here much longer."

Mark and Patrick backed into the opening in the rocks just as the bear let out another roar. He ran right toward Rich. "Look out, Rich! Here he comes!" Mark called.

Rich did not wait to see if the bear was coming or not. He just ran. When he reached the tunnel, he fell into the opening.

With a roar, the bear crashed into the tunnel mouth, fighting to get at the men. The dust was so heavy the men could hardly see.

"Man!" said Rich, as he fell back against the side of the tunnel. "He nearly had me."

The men looked around them. They saw that they were in a long tunnel. The tunnel was not very deep, and they could not turn around in it. They had to keep their heads down and back slowly down the dark tunnel.

"This had better be a way out of here," said Mark.

"That's for sure," Rich said. "We can't go back in there. Listen to that bear!" The men could hear the bear still trying to get at them through the mouth of the tunnel.

The men went on, their heads brushing against the sides of the tunnel. Cold drops of water ran down into their faces.

"How long do you think this tunnel is?" Rich asked.

"I don't know," said Mark, "but it's still going down."

"Listen!" said Patrick. The men stopped. They did not make any noise.

"What's up?" asked Mark, softly.

"I thought I heard something," said Patrick.

"Just the wind," said Mark. "Keep going."

The men went on. After a time the tunnel got bigger, and the men stood up. They found they could make their way along much faster now.

All of a sudden, Patrick, who was in the lead, stopped. The men had come out into another cave. The cave was so big that the men could not see the far side of it with their lights. They ran their lights over the dusty floor of the cave. There were marks there in the dust, as if something heavy had been pulled over it.

"That bear again?"
asked Rich.

"I don't think so," said
Patrick. "It looks like. . ."
Then he stopped. He pointed his light up and along
the side of the cave to his right. The rock there was
very dark and black. Then in the light they saw it—
wooden sticks for marking off a mine. They were all
over the floor.

"This is it!" Patrick called out.

"This is what?" asked Rich.

"I don't know how," Patrick said excitedly, "but
we have found Jim's mine. This is not a cave at all.
It's a uranium mine! Our uranium mine!"   (1204)

The End of a Ghost

Mark and Rich were surprised to see Patrick run this way and that around the cave calling, "We found it! We found it!" over and over again. The two younger men could not help but laugh at him.

Then the old miner stopped. "But did we?" he said to Mark and Rich.

"Did we what?" asked Rich.

"Well, this looks like the place," said Patrick, "but is this Jim's mine? I think we had better get out the Geiger-counters and see what they tell us about the rock in here."

"And another thing," said Mark. "If this is the place, where is the Geiger-counter that Jim had with him that day?"

"That's right!" said Patrick. "I had not thought about that."

"Come on, you two!" said Rich, now as excited as Patrick. "Let's see if this mine has good uranium ore or not!"

The three men lost no time at all in turning on their Geiger-counters. The counter sticks were pointed at the black rock. Right away they began to give back a hard and fast "click-click-click."

"That's money talking!" said Rich. "Man!"

Mark, who had walked a little way back into the cave, called out, "Rich! Patrick! Come here! Look what I found!"

The two men ran to his side. There in Mark's light, behind some rocks, they saw a wooden door leading into the side of the mine.

"A black door!" said Patrick in surprise.

"Black door, black door. Where have I heard that before?" said Rich.

"I have it!" said Mark. "Patrick, you said that your friend tried to tell you about 'black ore'. It was not 'black ore' at all. He was trying to tell you about a 'black door'."

"Well, now, it could have been a 'black door'," said the old man.

"Then Jim's Geiger-counter could be behind that door," said Rich.

Mark pulled on the heavy door, and it came open slowly. Pointing their lights into the tunnel behind it, the men looked around. There on the floor, behind some big rocks, was a Geiger-counter!

"This is it! This is the place!" said Patrick.

Suddenly the men heard a noise behind them. There was something coming toward them in the dark. They could feel it. The men turned around slowly.

There, back from the door, stood the ghostly being that Mark and Rich had seen the night before in Great Bear. Its great, lighted head nodded up and down in the dark. It never stopped. Its eyes, deep in its head, gave off a strange light.

Mark was not surprised by the ghost this time. Suddenly he pointed to a tunnel opening to the right and just behind the ghost. "Get him!" Mark called out, pointing his light right at the ghost.

The ghost turned its great head to face what was behind it.

"Now!" said Mark. With that, Mark and Rich ran right for the ghost. They reached it in no time, and crashed into the "thing," rocking it back with a hard blow. Down they went!

When Mark and Rich fell, their lights went out. The tunnel suddenly became very dark. They could not see at all. But even so, the two men could tell that this was not a ghost. It put up too good a fight. But the young men had been in fights before.

Patrick turned on his light just in time to see Rich crash a hard blow right into the ghost's mouth. The fight was over!

64

"I give up," said the man.

"Get up!" said Rich, as he backed away.

The man turned over on his back and got up slowly. There was dust all over him. Patrick pointed his light right into the man's eyes.

"Why, I know you," Patrick said. "You are one of the men who was after my friend Jim and the uranium mine he found."

"I don't know what you are talking about!" said the man.

"We think you do!" said Mark. "You are the one who tried to kill us out there on the trail."

The man was still. He looked at the three men. They stood close around him, watching with cold eyes. The man's head dropped. "All right, you got me," he said. "I did it. I wanted that uranium ore. After my friend gave up, I hunted through all these caves and tunnels. I even hunted through the cave on the other side of the mountain."

"How did you get away from the cave that day?" asked Mark.

"There is another opening in the back of the cave," said the man. "There's a trail leading down into Great Bear from there."

"How about last night in town," said Rich. "How did you pull off being a ghost?"

"I had been watching you from one of the buildings," said the man. "When you came looking for me, I just turned a light on my face and placed another one behind this animal hide I carried." The man pulled the hide up before him and turned on his light.

"Why it looks just like a ghost," said Rich.

"But how did you get away?" asked Mark.

"You did not see the big rock behind the hill," said the man. "It closed off the opening to an old gold mine. I was hiding there."

"You trailed us all the way here?" asked Patrick.

"When you left Great Bear, I was not far behind you," the man said. "But when that mine caved in, I thought you had been killed. Then the storm came up, and I had to get in out of it. I climbed into a tunnel, just like you did."

"You were right when you said that you heard something, Patrick," Mark said. "It was our friend here coming down the mine tunnel another way."

"Well, we had better get going," said Patrick. "We will have to turn this man in. Then we can come back here and place down our sticks to mark our find. Our country will want to know about this uranium."

"Just think of the money we will get," said Rich.

The three friends laughed. The noise climbed up the side of the mine and carried back into the deep, dark tunnels.

But one man did not laugh. There was nothing for him to laugh about. (1059)
7676

Vocabulary

The total vocabulary of this book is 282 words. Of these, 214 are below second grade and are not listed; 57 are second grade and appear below in roman type; 11 are above second grade and appear below in italic type. The numbers indicate the page on which the word first appears.

above 8
against 46

bad 5
bigger 54
brushing 6
building 30

can't 5
cave 8
cave-in 22
click 60
closer 13
colder 53
counter 60
crash 13

deep 7
done 21
dust 15

excitedly 11

faster 6
feeling 29
fighting 6
fire-blackened 33
friendly 10

given 13
ghost 7
gold 22

hardly 13
heavy 5
hunted 24

I'm 15
it's 5

kill 17

ladder 43
lead 26
listen 16

mark 24
mine 7
mountains 5

nearer 39
nearly 38
nodded 6

older 6
opening 8
ore 24

pointed 6

roaring 5
rocks 8
reached 7

sleepy 38
slower 8
slowly 18
snowy 30
softly 5
sooner 30
spot 7
stormed 5
strange 39
suddenly 11
sure 8

those 11
though 44
toward 8
trail 5
tunnels 26

uranium 7

without 21
wooden 59

young 5

* The number in parentheses on the last page of each chapter indicates the total number of words in that chapter. The number underlined on the last page of the story indicates the total number of words in the entire story.

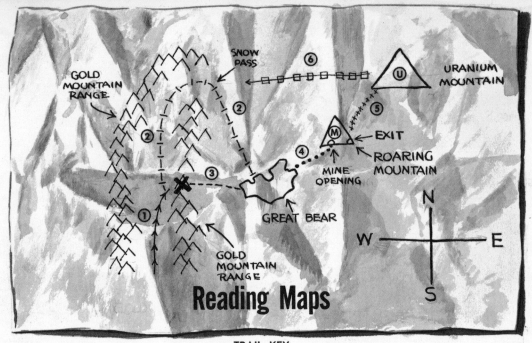

GOLD MOUNTAIN RANGE

SNOW PASS

① ② ③ ④ ⑤ ⑥

URANIUM MOUNTAIN

EXIT

ROARING MOUNTAIN

MINE OPENING

GREAT BEAR

GOLD MOUNTAIN RANGE

Reading Maps

N
W — E
S

TRAIL KEY

1 First Day Trail
2 Second Day Trail
3 Ghost Trail
4 Roaring Mt. Trail
5 Storm Trail

6 Uranium Ore Trail
X Ghost Cave
M Roaring Mountain
U Uranium Mountain

Mark and Patrick sat side by side in one of the buildings in Great Bear. On the floor before them was a map of the country where they had found the uranium ore. Rich stood over them, looking down at the map.

"The map looks good," said Rich. "But how are we going to get the uranium down out of the mountains?"

"Look here, Rich," said Mark, pointing to a spot on the map. "This is Uranium Mountain where we found the uranium ore. It's north and east of Roaring Mountain."

"I see that," said Rich. "Go on."

"We open a new trail from Uranium Mountain, Trail 6, that runs north of Roaring Mountain and west through Snow Pass. Then we can turn and move the ore south along Trail 2 and then Trail 1."

"Why not use the old trail we have?" asked Patrick. "We could carry the ore down Trail 5, go south of Roaring Mountain, and take Trail 4 into Great Bear."

"Then what?" asked Mark. "We would still have to move the ore north from Great Bear along Trail 2 and then through Snow Pass. Cutting that new trail, Trail 6, would be shorter in the long run."

"That does look best," said Rich. "Let's go!"

News Story

MINERS HUNT FOR URANIUM

DPI—The opening of a once lost uranium mine near the town of Great Bear in the Rocky Mountains has started a great hunt for uranium.

Men can be seen all through the hill country looking for the black ore that our country needs. A good ore find may bring a miner a lot of money.

A miner must go far back into the mountains to find uranium-bearing rock. He walks along the ground until he finds rocks that look like they have ore in them. Then he runs his Geiger-counter stick over them.

When the miner is sure that he has found uranium ore, he looks to see if someone has found the uranium ore before him. If he sees no sticks, he then marks the ore as his.

The miner works out where he thinks he will find the middle of the ore bed. First he walks along the bed, 750 feet each way from the middle. Then he walks off 300 feet on each side of the bed. Then he puts down wooden sticks, one at each of the four corners of the ore find and one at the middle of each of the two sides.

After the wooden sticks are put down, two other things must be done. First the miner must work his find before the end of 90 days. A wise miner works the find the first day so that others will see that he has been there. Then the miner must tell our country about his find. If he does not tell our country, other miners could take away his find.

Then the miner waits. He waits to see if his uranium find is a good one. He waits for our country to tell him how much money they will give him for his find.

"Tall Tales"

The miners who have worked for a long time in the mountains around Great Bear often tell stories about the long, cold winters they have seen. They tell these stories to make the younger men think that mining was harder in the old days. But were the winters as cold as the old miners say that they were? What do you think?

The winter of 1926 was very, very cold. There was more snow in the mountains than ever before. It snowed so hard that winter that all the animals had to run backwards to keep the snow out of their eyes.

It was very windy, too. One time, the "Ghost of Great Bear" opened his mouth to laugh. The wind was blowing so hard that it turned him inside out. But he did give some ghostly laughs that turned to ice and fell into the brush along the side of the trail. Some men walking along the trail saw the ghost laughs and carried them to their mines. When the laughs melted, the men frightened others away from the mines by dropping the laughs into the tunnel openings.

That winter there was a fire in one of the buildings in Great Bear. It was so cold that the water the men threw on the fire turned to ice. But that was all right. The fire had turned to ice, too!